C000129192

CONTENTS

Learning Songs

Supplementary Songs

Series Editor: Mark Mumford

Music arranged and processed by Barnes Music Engraving Ltd
East Sussex TN22 4HA, England

Cover Design by Headline Publicity Ltd, Chelmsford, Essex

Published 1995

INTRODUCTION

The Music About Us series aims to provide an essential library of topical resource material for Key Stage One and Key Stage Two pupils. The songs, together with the accompanying teaching ideas, are ideal for creating an immediate musical environment.

The Learning Songs are original, informative and fun to sing and perform. They provide thematic links to other subjects within the National Curriculum and will prove ideal for cross-curricular topic or project work. The use of the songs, and indeed much of the material in this series, will be dependent upon the age and ability of the children. In most cases however, the material is flexible enough to be adapted to deal with a number of requirements, thus providing the teacher with an ideal resource collection to 'dip into'.

Teaching Ideas provide initial suggestions for using the learning songs. They offer a variety of ways in which the songs may be performed, sometimes including ideas for actions, movement games and instrumental accompaniments. These suggestions can be combined to form a complete performance or simply selected to help with musical response and understanding. Their use will be dependent on key stage requirements.

The Musical Discussion notes offer further ideas and suggestions for exploring musical concepts. They provide initial points of discussion, sometimes concentrating on one specific musical element. There are many ways of developing these points but primarily they act as a basis for stimulating further work.

The Topical Discussion notes provide a series of leads enabling further exploration of the thematic content of the song. These are particularly useful for cross-curricular links within the National Curriculum, when applicable to the relevant key stage.

The Supplementary Song section offers a variety of songs, many of which may be well known. These songs may prove suitable for a number of uses, but as thematic material they can be used simply for singing. However, they can be developed by adding percussion accompaniments, actions etc.

Whether it is used to sing and learn about ourselves, how we live and the world around us, or as a basis for stimulating musical activity, the *Music About Us* series will undoubtedly prove a useful resource for music making in the classroom.

Driving In Our Car

Words and Music by
Bill Roberts and Mike Grocott

1 Get inside and close the door,
   Start the engine, hear it roar,
   Going off to see Grandma,
   Driving in our car.
   Lorry with a heavy load,
   Big wheels rolling down the road,
   Wonder if it's going far,
   Driving in our car.

   Brrm brrm brrm brrm, beep beep,
   Four wheels turning, beep beep,
   Brrm brrm brrm brrm, beep beep,
   Driving in our car.

2 See the people on the bus,
   They're all looking down on us,
   They go slow but we go fast,
   Driving in our car.
   Now we're in a traffic jam,
   Slowing down behind a van.
   We can't move 'cause we've just stopped
   Driving in our car.

   Brrm brrm brrm brrm, beep beep,
   Too much traffic, beep beep,
   Brrm brrm brrm brrm, beep beep,
   Driving in our car.

3 Motorbikes and bicycles,
   Milk-float with its milk bottles.
   See the tractor's muddy wheels,
   Driving in our car.
   Traffic-lights are straight ahead,
   Got to stop, they've changed to red.
   Off we go, they're green again,
   Driving in our car.

   Brrm brrm brrm brrm, beep beep,
   Red light, green light, beep beep,
   Brrm brrm brrm brrm, beep beep,
   Driving in our car.

4 Zebra-crossing coming up,
   People waiting, so we stop,
   Headlights on, it's getting dark,
   Driving in our car.
   Windscreen-wipers swish the rain,
   Check the map, we're lost again,
   Find the B3213,
   Driving in our car.

   Brrm brrm brrm brrm, beep beep,
   Use the road map, beep beep,
   Brrm brrm brrm brrm, beep beep,
   Driving in our car.

TEACHING IDEAS

A song about a journey in a car and the forms of transport that are passed along the way.

Actions

There are various actions that children can perform in this song. Here are a few:

Driving in our car   – Pretend to use a steering wheel
Four wheels turning – Circular action with hand
Too much traffic   – Hand on forehead
Windscreen wipers   – Move arm like a windscreen wiper

During the second verse the children should get quieter from the point marked 'half tempo'. 'Stopped' should be whispered.

Accompaniments

Add sound effects to the chorus.

For example:

Scraper

Brrm brrm brrm brrm

Car horn

Beep beep

Sound effects can also be added throughout the verses.

For example:

Verse 1

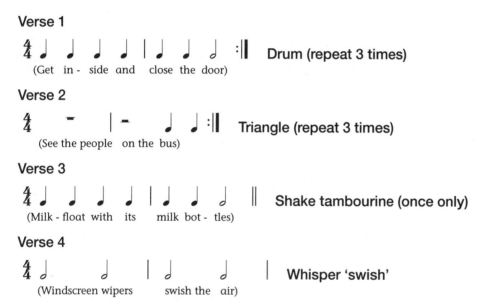

Drum (repeat 3 times)

(Get in - side and close the door)

Verse 2

Triangle (repeat 3 times)

(See the people on the bus)

Verse 3

Shake tambourine (once only)

(Milk - float with its milk bot - tles)

Verse 4

Whisper 'swish'

(Windscreen wipers swish the air)

Musical Discussion

Ask the children to list the different types of transport in the song, with the loudest sounding ones at the top and the quietest at the bottom. Then get them to match a percussion instrument to each type of transport (perhaps using examples from the accompaniment). If a group of children are lined up in a row, can they organise themselves so that the loudest sounds are at one end and the quietest at the other? Can they re-arrange the list so that the faster forms of transport are at the top and the slower ones at the bottom?

Get the children to retell this journey by recording the real sounds that these forms of transport make. Divide the children into groups and give each group a verse to record. For sounds that are either too difficult or too dangerous to obtain, record a percussion instrument instead.

Topical Discussion

Discuss the similarities between the different types of transport mentioned in the song, e.g. they can all be found on roads, they all have wheels, etc. What are the differences (using pictures may help)? Why do some types of transport go faster than others? What are different forms of transport used for? How do they change direction? Have the children been in a traffic jam? What causes traffic jams? Discuss different types of roads. What do traffic lights do and what do the different colours mean? Is there a road near the school? How do the children cross it? How do maps help us? Can the children draw a map of their route to school? Use pictures to mark out the route.

Round And Round

Words and Music by
Bill Roberts and Mike Grocott

1   Two wheels on my bicycle,
    Going round, round and round,
    Two wheels on my bicycle,
    Going round and round.

2   Pedals turn the chain around,
    Up and down, round and round,
    Pedals turn the chain around,
    Going round and round.

3   Legs push the pedals,
    Turn the chain, turns the back wheel round,
    Going round and round, and round and round.

4   If you're on your bike one day,
    And there's someone in your way,
    Blow your horn or ring your bell,
    Make a warning sound.

5   (instrumental)

6   Hands on the handle-bars
    Turn the front wheel left or right,
    Going round and round, and round and round.

7   Fingers on the brake-levers,
    Squeeze them tight to slow the bike,
    Brake pads push against the wheels,
    Stops them going round.

8   Pump the tyres up with air,
    Check the spokes, and oil the gears,
    Be seen at night, turn on your lights
    When you're riding round.

9   Two wheels on my bicycle,
    Going round, round and round,
    Two wheels on my bicycle,
    Going round and round.

TEACHING IDEAS

A song about the bicycle and the parts that make it work.

Actions

Verse 1	*Going round and round*	–	Draw circles in the air with a finger
Verse 2	*Pedals turn the chain around*	–	Rotating action with arms
Verse 3	*Legs push pedals*	–	March on the spot
Verse 4	*If you're on your bike one day*	–	Pretend to ride a bicycle moving up and down
Verse 6	*Turn the front wheel left or right*	–	Move to left then to right
Verse 7	*Fingers on the brake-levers*	–	Pretend to squeeze brakes
Verse 8	*Pump the tyres up with air*	–	Pumping action
Verse 9	(as verse 1)		

Accompaniments

Use verse 5 as an instrumental verse:

Recorders

Triangles

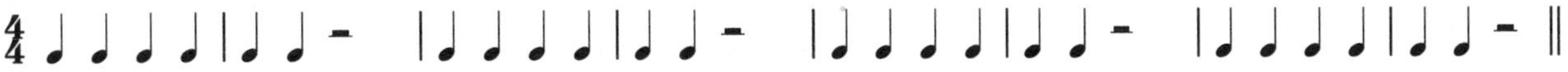

Tambourines

Car Horn

Whistle

Topical Discussion

Ask the children to describe a bicycle. What are they used for? How do they work? What happens when the pedals are pushed? How does the bike slow down? Talk about the 'hobby-horse' bicycle of the early 19th Century. How useful are bicycles? What other types of bicycles are there (e.g. Unicycle, tricycle)? How many wheels do they have? Discuss how the wheels of a bike spin or rotate around an axle.

Discuss safety on a bicycle and how a bike must be looked after.

On The Water

Words and Music by
Bill Roberts and Mike Grocott

1. Big ships sail a - cross the o - cean
2. Tu - dor ships had masts and rig - ging,
3. Maps and charts for na - vi - ga - tion,
4. Sail - ing boats of diff - erent siz - es,
5. Fish - er - man sit - ting still and qui - et,

tak - ing things a - round the world.
Vi - king ships had lots of oars.
years a - go, they used the stars.
set the sails to catch the wind.
in his boat out on the lake,

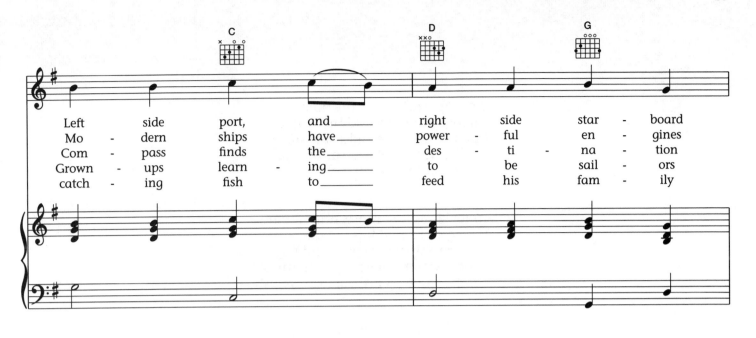

Left side port, and right side star - board
Mo - dern ships have power - ful en - gines
Com - pass finds the des - ti - na - tion
Grown - ups learn - ing to be sail - ors
catch - ing fish to feed his fam - ily

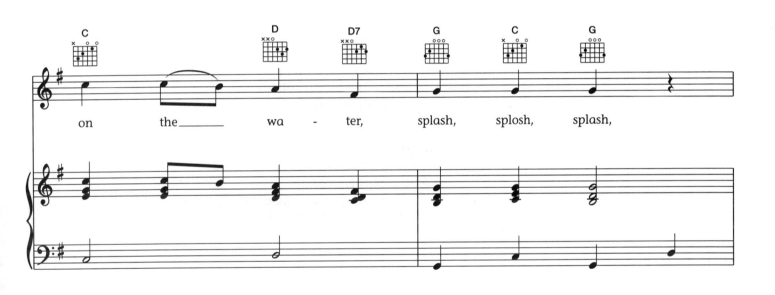

on the wa - ter, splash, splosh, splash,

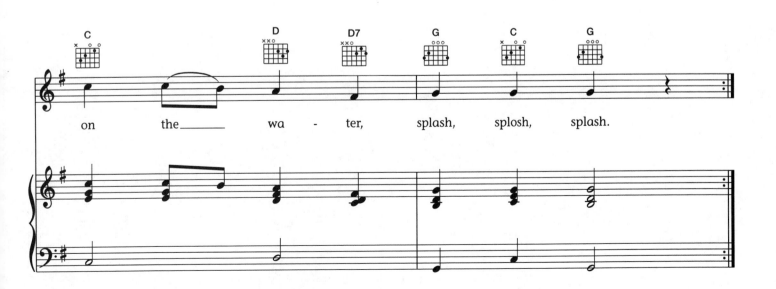

on the wa - ter, splash, splosh, splash.

1 Big ships sail across the ocean
  Taking things around the world.
  Left side port and right side starboard
  On the water, splash, splosh, splash,
  On the water, splash, splosh, splash.

2 Tudor ships had masts and rigging,
  Viking ships had lots of oars.
  Modern ships have powerful engines
  On the water, splash, splosh, splash,
  On the water, splash, splosh, splash.

3 Maps and charts for navigation,
  Years ago they used the stars.
  Compass finds the destination
  On the water, splash, splosh, splash,
  On the water, splash, splosh, splash.

4 Sailing boats of different sizes
  Set the sails to catch the wind.
  Grown-ups learning to be sailors
  On the water, splash, splosh, splash,
  On the water, splash, splosh, splash.

5 Fisherman sitting still and quiet,
  In his boat out on the lake,
  Catching fish to feed his family
  On the water, splash, splosh, splash,
  On the water, splash, splosh, splash.

TEACHING IDEAS

A descriptive and informative song about travelling on the water.

Actions

Verse 1	*Left side port and right side starboard*	–	Turn and hold out arms in appropriate direction
Verse 2	*Viking ships had lots of oars*	–	Pretend to row
Verse 3	*Years ago they used the stars*	–	Move hand to forehead and look up at the stars
Verse 4	*Set the sails to catch the wind*	–	Move hands to imitate a boat bobbing on the waves
Verse 5	*Catching fish to feed his family*	–	Pretend to fish with rod

Accompaniments

Tambourine and shaker

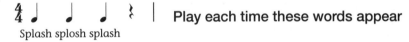

Splash splosh splash   Play each time these words appear

Glockenspiels (verses – i.e. not introduction)

Musical Discussion

Ask the children to describe the sounds that some of the boats in the song would make. Ask them to imitate the sounds vocally.

Explain the points of a compass and give each point a percussion sound. Ask the children to move in the direction that each sound represents. This can be expanded so that the sounds become beats. Each beat would mean taking a step in the relevant direction.

For example:

North – Triangle
South – Drum
East – Scraper
West – Claves

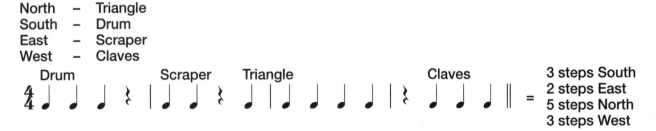

3 steps South
2 steps East
5 steps North
3 steps West

This game can also be adapted to use dynamics, note values or rhythmic / melodic patterns, to determine the different directions.

Music played a big part on ships in days gone by. Play and sing some sea-shanties (e.g. *A-Roving, Blow The Man Down, What Shall We Do With The Drunken Sailor,* etc.). What are they about?

Topical Discussion

Talk about different types of boats and ships. What are they used for? How important were they in the past? How have boats changed throughout the ages? How does a ship float? What makes a boat move and how does it change direction? What does *navigate* mean? Collect some pictures of different ships and boats.

The Children's Learning Railway

Words and Music by
Bill Roberts and Mike Grocott

Moderately, with a swing

1. We're on the child - ren's learn - ing
(3.) child - ren's learn - ing

rail - way, and it's twen - ty coach - es long, an
rail - way, got our tic - kets in our hands.

old steam en - gine's pull - ing us, built so big and
We can go long dis - tan - ces at high speeds o - ver

1   We're on the children's learning railway,
    And it's twenty coaches long,
    An old steam engine's pulling us,
    Built so big and strong.
    Rolling down the railway tracks,
    Through the countryside.
    We're on the children's learning railway,
    And everyone can take a ride.

2   Back in 1825
    A man called Stephenson
    Built an engine powered by steam,
    Locomotion Number One.
    No more horses pulling coaches
    On the railway-lines,
    The locomotion engine could
    Do the job in half the time.

3   We're on the children's learning railway,
    Got our tickets in our hands.
    We can go long distances
    At high speeds over land.
    Fast electric engines take us far and wide.
    We're on the children's learning railway,
    And everyone can take a ride.

4   In London and New York,
    There are railways underground
    Beneath the busy city streets,
    Helping people get around.
    Bridges span the big wide rivers
    So the trains can cross,
    And the signals tell the drivers
    That the way ahead is clear for us.

5   We're on the children's learning railway,
    Leaving platform number nine,
    Taking people, goods and mail
    To stops along the line.
    Steam and diesel and electric
    Trains are used worldwide.
    We're on the children's learning railway,
    And everyone can take a ride.

TEACHING IDEAS

A song that gives an insight into the history of the train.

Accompaniments

Verse 1

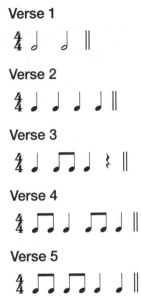

Verse 2

Verse 3

Verse 4

Verse 5

Repeat the rhythm throughout the verse. Choose a different percussion instrument to match each verse. It may be useful to divide the children into five groups.

Musical Discussion

Keeping the children in their five groups, explore the accompaniment rhythm a little further. Create a cumulative rhythmic exercise. Set a pulse and gradually introduce each group, once the previous group have played their exercise four times. Clap the rhythms at first and then replace with percussion instruments. The effect should be that of a train starting out on its journey and gradually picking up speed. Try to get the children to start quietly and gradually get louder as each new group enters. Discuss the rhythms. Who played long notes? Who played short ones? Can the exercise be reversed so that the train stops?

In pairs, ask the children to paint a picture of a train journey, including all the things that they might see. Using a variety of resources ask them to perform their journey in sound. What did they pass on their journey? Did they go through any tunnels? One child can imitate the train, whilst the other adds the sounds of the objects or scenes that are passed on the journey. Remember that there should always be a start and finish to the journey. This allows for gradation of speed and dynamics. This idea can be used as a whole class topic with each child providing a picture and sound for each stage of the journey. The rhythmic exercise (above) could be used once again to imitate the train.

Topical Discussion

The first passenger trains were in 1825. How did they start to effect peoples lives? Who was George Stephenson? How did people travel long distances before passenger trains were invented? What were the first trains called? Talk about the different types of trains and track systems used in different countries. What is a freight train? What type of things do trains transport? Discuss railway stations and underground stations.

How do trains move? Have the children travelled on trains? Where did they go?

Orville And Wilbur Wright

Words and Music by
Bill Roberts and Mike Grocott

Thank you ve-ry much Or-ville and Wil-bur Wright.

1   Orville and Wilbur Wright built the first aeroplane
To take off, fly and land on the ground again.
It didn't fly very high,
But it was only their first try.
Thank you very much Orville and Wilbur Wright.

2   Now there are Jumbo jets flying round the world
At 35,000 feet, like a silverbird.
Big jet-engines on the wings,
Running on a fuel called kerosene.
Thank you very much Orville and Wilbur Wright

3   You can travel really far in a fast aeroplane today,
Far away places don't seem so far away.
If you're out there having fun,
On a holiday in the sun,
Say 'Thank you very much Orville and Wilbur Wright'.

4   Rocket-ships blast off – 5-4-3-2-1,
Helicopters hover, rotor blades whirling around.
Take a trip in a hot air balloon
On a Sunday afternoon.
Oh, and thank you very much Orville and Wilbur Wright.

5   Take some paper, glue and sticky-tape,
Make your own aeroplane and design its shape,
And when you hear a plane fly by,
Just look up in the sky
And say 'Thank you very much Orville and Wilbur Wright'.

TEACHING IDEAS

A song that highlights the achievements of Orville and Wilbur Wright, and introduces different forms of air transport.

Accompaniments

Thank you ve - ry much Or - ville and Wil - bur Wright.

Last line of each verse

Play on untuned percussion instruments. Change percussion instruments for each verse.

Musical Discussion

Ask the children to identify the different flying machines in this song. What sounds do they make? Talk about low and high sounds and demonstrate using a piano. Discuss how sound can gradually get higher. Play a glissando on the piano or on a xylophone. Get the children to crouch and rise very slowly as a scale is being played on the piano.

Collect pictures of different forms of transport. Arrange them on a wall and label them with musical elements. These could be a mixture of high/low sounds, long/short sounds or of dynamics. Ask the children to react using percussion instruments to each picture as it is pointed to.

Pick some important dates in transport development and if possible some pictures to illustrate the different forms. Try to find music and songs that would have been popular at the same time. Arrange both sets of material chronologically. Look at and discuss the changes that have taken place in both transport and music and the effect that they have had on people's lives.

Topical Discussion

Ask the children to name and describe the types of transport in the song. Can they think of any others? Discuss what different types of transport are used for. Have any of the children travelled on a plane? What did it feel like? What effect has air travel had on people's lives? How does an aeroplane take off? How does it change direction? How does a helicopter change direction?

Safety

Words and Music by
Bill Roberts and Mike Grocott

1   Trains and cars and boats and planes
And lorries follow a safety code.
Look right, look left, look right again,
Every time you're crossing the road.

Safety, safety, gotta think safety,
Gotta think safety every time,
Safety, safety, gotta think safety,
Gotta think safety every time.

2   Don't forget to fasten your seat-belt
Every time you get in a car,
And if you're ever out on a dark night,
Don't forget, wear something light.

Safety, safety, gotta think safety,
Gotta think safety every time,
Safety, safety, gotta think safety,
Gotta think safety every time.

3   Trains and cars and boats and planes
And lorries follow a safety code.
Look right, look left, look right again,
Every time you're crossing the road.

Safety, safety, gotta think safety,
Gotta think safety every time,
Safety, safety, gotta think safety,
Gotta think safety every time,
Gotta think safety every time.

TEACHING IDEAS

A useful song that can be sung in unison or as a round.

Accompaniments

Repeat throughout verses and choruses

First time   –   Triangle
Second time –   Triangle and Tambourine
Third time   –   Triangle, Tambourine and Drum

Recorders (Chorus)

Musical Discussion

Discuss warning sounds. How many can the children think of? What do they sound like? What do they tell us? Use vocal sounds to describe them.

Play echo games using words and rhythms from the song.

For example:

look   right a - gain,   Got - ta think safe - ty

Ask the children to clap, sing and play the echoes.

Topical Discussion

Discuss the Green Cross Code. Talk about the devices that exist to protect travellers, e.g. seatbelts, lifebelts, etc. How do traffic lights and railway signal boxes help? How do different types of transport deal with darkness and bad weather conditions?

The Wheels On The Bus

Traditional

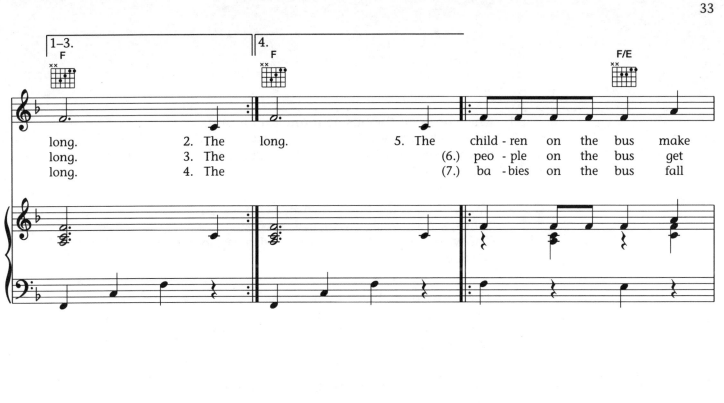
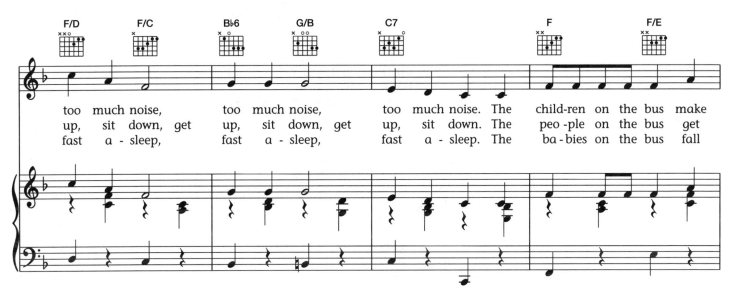
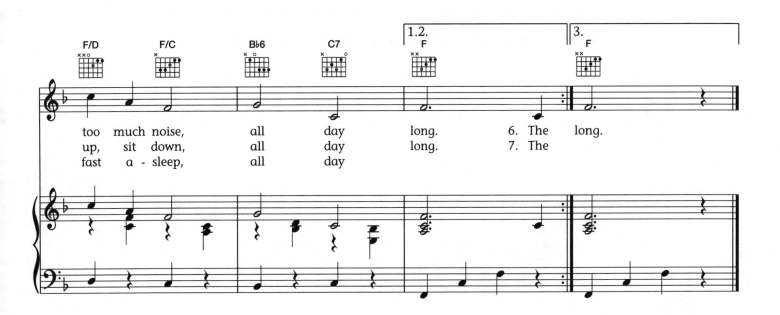

1 The wheels on the bus go round and round,
Round and round, round and round.
The wheels on the bus go round and round,
All day long.

2 The wipers on the bus go swish, swish, swish,
Swish, swish, swish, swish, swish, swish.
The wipers on the bus go swish, swish, swish,
All day long.

3 The horn on the bus goes beep, beep, beep,
Beep, beep, beep, beep, beep, beep.
The horn on the bus goes beep, beep, beep,
All day long.

4 The bell on the bus goes ding, ding, ding,
Ding, ding, ding, ding, ding, ding.
The bell on the bus goes ding, ding, ding,
All day long.

5 The children on the bus make too much noise,
Too much noise, too much noise.
The children on the bus make too much noise,
All day long.

6 The people on the bus get up, sit down,
Get up, sit down, get up, sit down.
The people on the bus get up, sit down,
All day long.

7 The babies on the bus fall fast asleep,
Fast asleep, fast asleep.
The babies on the bus fall fast asleep,
All day long.

An ideal action song with lots of opportunities for sound effects.

Morningtown Ride

Words and Music by
Malvina Reynolds

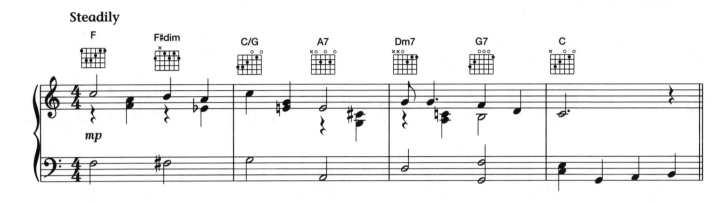

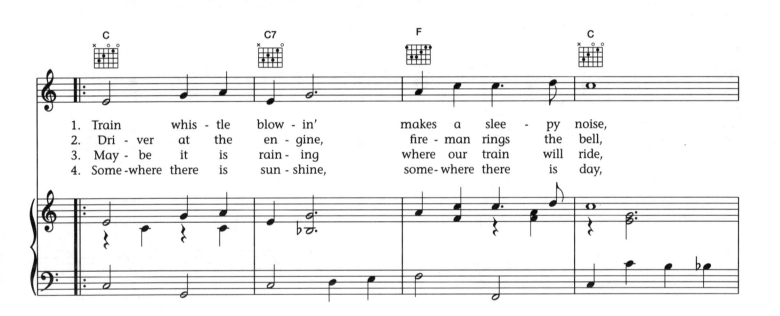

1. Train whis-tle blow-in' makes a slee-py noise,
2. Dri-ver at the en-gine, fire-man rings the bell,
3. May-be it is rain-ing where our train will ride,
4. Some-where there is sun-shine, some-where there is day,

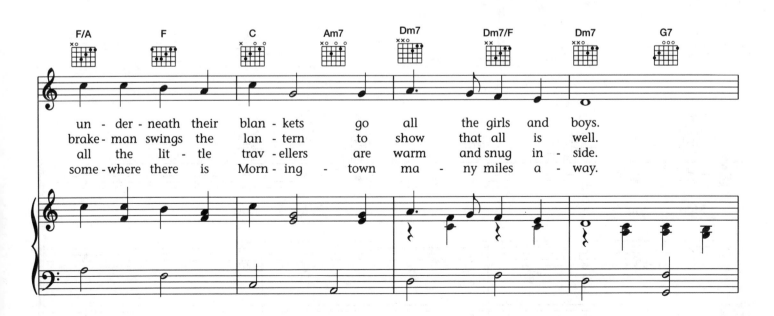

un-der-neath their blan-kets go all the girls and boys.
brake-man swings the lan-tern to show that all is well.
all the lit-tle trav-ellers are warm and snug in-side.
some-where there is Morn-ing-town ma-ny miles a-way.

1   Train whistle blowin' makes a sleepy noise,
    Underneath their blankets go all the girls and boys.
    Rockin', rollin', ridin', out along the bay,
    All bound for Morningtown many miles away.

2   Driver at the engine, fireman rings the bell,
    Brake-man swings the lantern to show that all is well.
    Rockin', rollin', ridin', out along the bay,
    All bound for Morningtown many miles away.

3   Maybe it is raining where our train will ride,
    All the little travellers are warm and snug inside.
    Rockin', rollin', ridin', out along the bay,
    All bound for Morningtown many miles away.

4   Somewhere there is sunshine, somewhere there is day,
    Somewhere there is Morningtown many miles away.
    Rockin', rollin', ridin', out along the bay,
    All bound for Morningtown many miles away,
    All bound for Morningtown many miles away.

Sleigh Ride

Words by Mitchell Parish
Music by Leroy Anderson

Just hear those sleigh bells jingling,
Ring ting tingling too.
Come on, it's lovely weather
For a sleigh ride together with you.

Outside the snow is falling,
And friends are calling 'Yoo hoo!'
Come on, it's lovely weather
For a sleigh ride together with you.

Giddy yap, giddy yap,
Giddy yap, let's go,
Let's look at the show,
We're riding in a wonderland of snow.

Giddy yap, giddy yap,
Giddy yap, it's grand,
Just holding your hand,
We're gliding along with a song of a wintery fairy land.

Our cheeks are nice and rosy,
And comfy cosy are we.
We're snuggled up together
Like two birds of a feather would be.

Let's take that road before us,
And sing a chorus or two.
Come on, it's lovely weather
For a sleigh ride together with you.

Add lots of sleigh bells to this song. A useful song to introduce how certain weather conditions can necessitate alternative forms of transport.

The Runaway Train

Words by Robert E Massey
Music by Carson Robison

'Twas in the year of eighty-nine,
On that old Chicago line,
When the winter wind was blowin' shrill.
The rails were froze,
The wheels were cold,
Then the air brakes wouldn't hold,
And number nine came roarin' down the hill.

1   Oh! The runaway train came down the track, and she blew, she blew.
    The runaway train came down the track, and she blew, she blew.
    The runaway train came down the track,
    Her whistle wide and her throttle back,
    And she blew, blew, blew, blew, blew.

2   The engineer said the train must halt and she blew, she blew.
    The engineer said the train must halt and she blew, she blew.
    The engineer said the train must halt,
    He said it was all the fireman's fault,
    And she blew, blew, blew, blew, blew.

3   The fireman said he rang the bell and she blew, she blew.
    The fireman said he rang the bell and she blew, she blew.
    The fireman said he rang the bell,
    The engineer said it's just as well,
    And she blew, blew, blew, blew, blew.

This song certainly needs a whistle blower! Try singing as is written until 'Oh! The runaway train...' From then on each line should be treated as a crescendo, i.e. every line starting *pp* and ending f, until the end of the song.

The Pushbike Song

Words and Music by
Idris Jones and Evan Jones

1. Rid-ing a-long__ on my push-bike hon-ey,
2. Put on the speed_ and I tried catch-ing up, but you were
3. Rid-ing a-long__ on a bi-cy-cle hon-ey, that's a

when I no-ticed you.__   Rid-ing down-town__ in a
pe-dal-ling hard-er too.__   Rid-ing a-long__ like a
bi-cy-cle built_ for two.__   Look-ing at my hon-ey in the

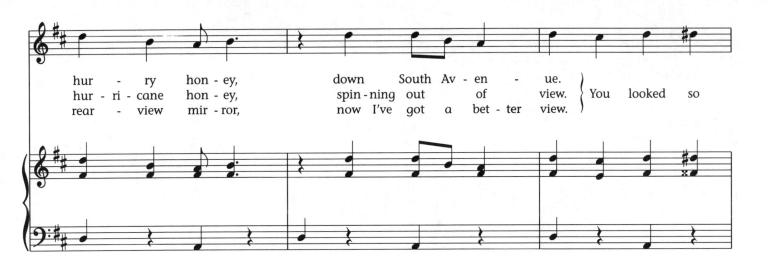

hur - ry hon - ey, down South Av - en - ue.
hur - ri - cane hon - ey, spin - ning out of view. } You looked so
rear - view mir - ror, now I've got a bet - ter view.

pret - ty as you were rid - ing a - long._____ You looked so

pret - ty as you were sing - ing this song._____

1   Riding along on my pushbike honey,
When I noticed you.
Riding down-town in a hurry honey,
Down South Avenue.
You looked so pretty as you were riding along.
You looked so pretty as you were singing this song.

Round, round wheels going round, round, round,
Down, up, pedals down, up, down,
But I got to get across to the other side of town
Before the sun goes down.
Hey hey hey!

2   Put on the speed and I tried catching up,
But you were pedalling harder too.
Riding along like a hurricane honey,
Spinning out of view.
You looked so pretty as you were riding along.
You looked so pretty as you were singing this song.

Round, round wheels going round, round, round,
Down, up, pedals down, up, down,
But I got to get across to the other side of town
Before the sun goes down.
Hey hey hey!

3   Riding along on a bicycle honey,
That's a bicycle built for two.
Looking at my honey in the rear-view mirror,
Now I've got a better view.
You looked so pretty as you were riding along.
You looked so pretty as you were singing this song.

Round, round wheels going round, round, round,
Down, up, pedals down, up, down,
But I got to get across to the other side of town
Before the sun goes down.
Hey hey hey!

A topical song ideal for adding percussion, sound effects and actions.

Ferry-Boat Serenade

Words by Harold Adamson
Music by E di Lazzaro

I have ne - ver been a - board a steam - er,

I am just con - tent to be a dream - er,

ev - en if I could af - ford a steam - er,

G7   Cm

Hap - py   as we cling to - ge - ther,   hap - py   as we sing to - ge - ther,

G7   Dm7♭5   G7   Cm   1.   G7   2.

hap - py   with a   fer - ry-boat se - re - nade.

I have never been aboard a steamer,
I am just content to be a dreamer,
Even if I could afford a steamer,
I will take the ferry-boat all the time.
I love to ride the ferry
Where music is so merry.
There's a man who plays the concertina
On the moonlit upper deck arena
While boys and girls are dancing,
While sweethearts are romancing.
Life is like a Mardi Gras,
Funiculi, funicula.
Happy as we cling together,
Happy as we sing together,
Happy with a ferry-boat serenade.

A useful topical song . . . and just what is a 'funicula'?

On The Atchison, Topeka And The Santa Fe

Words by Johnny Mercer
Music by Harry Warren

Moderate shuffle

1. Do you hear that whis-tle down the line?___ I
(2.) ol' smoke ris-in' 'round the bend,___ I

fig - ure that it's en - gine num - ber for - ty nine.___ She's the
rec - kon that she knows she's gon - na meet a friend.___ Folks a -

1   Do you hear that whistle down the line?
    I figure that it's engine number forty nine.
    She's the only one that'll sound the way
    On the Atchison, Topeka and the Santa Fe.

2   See the ol' smoke risin' 'round the bend,
    I reckon that she knows she's gonna meet a friend.
    Folks around these parts get the time o' day
    From the Atchison, Topeka and the Santa Fe.

    Here she comes, (*whistle*) ooo ooo ooo.
    Hey Jim you better get the rig, (*whistle*) ooo ooo ooo.
    She's got a list of passengers that's pretty big,
    And they'll all want lifts to Brown's Hotel,
    'Cause lots of them been travellin' for quite a spell,
    All the way from Philadelphiay,
    On the Atchison, Topeka and the Santa Fe.

An ideal song for adding percussion instruments.

Those Magnificent Men In Their Flying Machines

Words and Music by
Ron Goodwin

Those magnificent men in their flying machines,
They go up tiddle-ee up up,
They go down tiddle-ee-own down.
They enchant all the ladies and steal all the scenes,
With their up tiddle-ee up ups,
And their down tiddle-ee-own downs.
Up, down, flying around,
Looping the loop and defying the ground.
They're all frightfully keen,
Those magnificent men in their flying machines.

They can fly upside down with their feet in the air,
They don't think of danger, they really don't care,
Newton would think he had made a mistake
To see those young men and the chances they take.

Those magnificent men in their flying machines,
They go up tiddle-ee up up,
They go down tiddle-ee-own down.
They enchant all the ladies and steal all the scenes,
With their up tiddle-ee up ups,
And their down tiddle-ee-own downs.
Up, down, flying around,
Looping the loop and defying the ground.
They're all frightfully keen,
Those magnificent men,
Those magnificent men,
Those magnificent men in their flying machines.

Lots of opportunities for actions in this song. Particularly useful for exploring high and low sounds.

Printed by
Halstan & Co. Ltd., Amersham, Bucks., England